From PIE to IEP

Peggy Howard

Trilogy Christian Publishers
A Wholly Owned Subsidary of Trinity Broadcasting Network
2442 Michelle Drive
Tustin, CA 92780

Cover design by: Cornerstone Creative Solutions

For information, address Trilogy Christian Publishing
Rights Department, 2442 Michelle Drive, Tustin, Ca 92780.
Trilogy Christian Publishing/ TBN and colophon are trademarks of Trinity Broadcasting Network.

For information about special discounts for bulk purchases, please contact Trilogy Christian Publishing.

Manufactured in the United States of America

10 9 8 7 6 5 4 3 2 1

Library of Congress Cataloging-in-Publication Data is available.

ISBN 978-1-63769-240-0 (Print Book)
ISBN 978-1-63769-241-7 (ebook)

Peggy Howard is one of those rare individuals who stands out in the education profession. Her exceptional ability to meet the needs of each of her special students while counseling their parents as they face unexpected challenges is remarkable. Her ability to motivate for excellence is always present whether in the classroom, in Special Olympics, or as the school's basketball coach for both boys and girls. Success and participation is not for a select few but for every student.
—Dr. James D. Upchurch, Dr. Linda L. Upchurch

Twenty-seven years ago, as the assistant principal and later principal, I had the privilege to hire one of the best special education teachers a school could have and was able to work with her for seventeen years. Peggy Howard was a compassionate and empathetic teacher, who knew how to get the most from her students and help their parents along the way while following their IEP. Peggy has written the book to continue educating both children and parents in the process one must go through for an IEP, from beginning to end. What is so wonderful is that she has written this book in a way that also show the humor in this process.
Please enjoy this book that Peggy has so lovingly written.
—Geri Sullivan-Ficken

Dedication

Dedicated to my children Andrew and Kadie, who I love unconditionally.

"Welcome Back to School" the sign read, I can't wait or can I…I think I'm ready. I have my pink and gray polka dot backpack packed with all my new school supplies and my matching lunch box. My first-day outfit is a gray pair of skinny jeans, with a long short-sleeved flowery orange shirt. Looking in the mirror I think I look ready, then dad walks by my room and says, "Honey, you are beautiful with anything you wear." Why does dad always say that?

So, if I look ready, why do I not feel ready? The other night I could not go to sleep because my mind just wouldn't shut off. Does your mind ever do that? Anyway, I just kept thinking about *will this be the year I can read faster, write sentences correctly, and spell better*? And what about the D.O. L. (Daily Oral Language) sentences? They get me every time.

I am so tired of the teacher's red marks; I could just scream all night. I try really hard. I study with my mom, but something always goes wrong on test day.

Well, here I am, the first day of school and we are having a scavenger hunt. I need to find where the glue sticks tub is located to finish the game. I told my friend this game is A-W-E-S-O-M-E! Now we are playing "Have you ever" and it is *super* fun! "Class, Class," the teacher said, and we shouted back "Yes! Yes!" Then she started talking.

"We all have beautiful voices that were made to talk, but when I want to talk, I will say: Three, two beautiful eyes looking at me," and then she whispers, "One voice is all you shall hear." Boy, do I like her! When she talks like this, I smile from my head to my toes. Next, she asks us how much "think time" we need when we are working in math. We can show her one, two, or three fingers representing minutes and she says she will wait whatever we show her. We all start laughing because we have never had a teacher do this before.

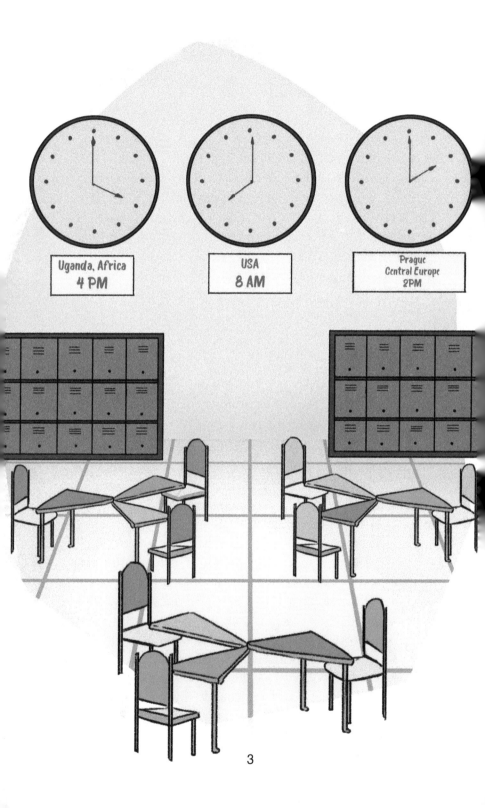

Uganda, Africa
4 PM

USA
8 AM

Prague
Central Europe
2PM

3

Now she says it is time for *Triple T*! *Yikes*, I thought. We are moving our desks into a triangle. Now sit, and place your elbows on your desktop and lean in like you are going to talk to each other. This is our Triple T time…table talk time! This day just keeps getting better and better. This sure has been a great morning. I can't wait to see what the cafeteria looks like.

BE a
FRIEND
☺
SHARE a
TABLE

Today's
Lunch

* Corndogs *
* Tatertots *
* Corn *
* Apple Sauce *
* Brownie *

- choice -
Milk or Juice

Wow! It's huge, there are colored banners everywhere even hanging from the ceiling. My friend and I look at each other and say, "Can you believe this? We can sit anywhere we want to." The teacher told us we had to use our "just right" voice if we wanted to sit next to each other. Well, I wasn't sure what she meant about a "just right" voice level, so I asked her. She said, "Do this, stick your arms straight out, see where your elbows are? That is considered the just right voice level." My voice cannot be louder than that. It sure seems silly to me but whatever this is the best day ever. After lunch, we have recess then go back to class.

"It's math time," she says, "so get out your math toolbox." She made a math toolbox for all of us and put them in our desks while we were at lunch. She's a sneaky peaky teacher!

She says, "Open them up and tell me what you find." I couldn't believe it, there is a white paper ruler, a bag of plastic coins, adding and subtracting flashcards, a huge pink eraser, and a yellow paper clock.

The teacher had given us numbers right after the first bell this morning and my number was twelve. She told us if our number was even to find a classmate who had an odd number. Well, that took a little while since we kind of forgot what odd and even numbers were. But she helped us partner up and soon we were practicing our addition flashcards and slightly giggling, too.

While I was putting the flashcards back in the math toolbox, I remembered a time when mom and dad were helping me in math. Mom let me use her buttons from her button jar and dad let me use his pens and pencils from his office desk. Okay, back to class, I forget to keep listening to the teacher sometimes. I'm not sure what she said but this is what I heard next, "and now let's put away our math tools and pack up its time to go home." *Home*? Really? Best day ever!

AT HOME

Mom starts with her hundred questions as soon as the back-door closes, "So Little Bit (that's what she calls me sometimes, it's okay) what was the favorite part of your day?"

"Well," I said, "First it was recess because I was swinging so high like a bird soaring through a bunch of rain clouds. Then we used real paintbrushes and painted a picture using all our favorite colors. You know my favorite colors are orange and pink, don't you mom?"

Mom just nodded her head, "What else did you do?"

Reading time

Autobiography

Non-fiction

Picture Book

Chapter Book

Manual

Recipe Card

Fiction

"I listened to both fiction and nonfiction stories. My favorite stories were nonfiction. My favorite story was about Narwhals and my second favorite story was about space and being an astronaut. She told us her dad use to fly airplanes in the Air Force but doesn't fly anymore. Mom, did you know Narwhals can live up to fifty years old and the oldest astronaut to go into space was seventy-seven years old? *Wow*! Wonder what you can do mom when you're 77!" She just giggled.

And now, my friends, here's the real story about me and school. If the teacher asks me to read aloud, it takes me a very long time to read. Some kids even start laughing at me. A teacher once told me to hurry up, he didn't have all morning! I wanted to say, "Trust me, I would if I could." My mind thinks ▣ is ▣ and *bic* is really *bike*. It doesn't matter if I sit near the teacher or far away. Sometimes, the teachers will accuse me of daydreaming or not paying attention, but that's not true. It's really not.

Chromebook Cart

13

I do not mind reading center time, because I can build words with my best friend, play a word game on the iPad, or read a story on IXL Chromebook. If I could ever finish my center work, I could have some free time on the computer but that rarely happens.

Well, one day in art class the art teacher told us to paint our favorite Thanksgiving dessert. That was easy, draw a large triangle, color it brown with white fluffy clouds on top and there it was. I love, love, love, love, love, pumpkin pie! Mom and dad taped the picture on the refrigerator with a sign, "*Future Artist*". I'm not sure I believe them, but it makes them smile.

The very next week my teacher gave me an envelope for mom and dad and said it was a nice note and not to worry. I like it when she smiles at me. I told them the teacher said it was a good note when I handed it to them. They first read the note to themselves and then they read it to me. The teacher would like to meet with them on Friday.

What? Friday? Did I win something, or earn a huge award for my pumpkin pie drawing, or passed my 8's subtraction facts. I could barely sleep all week.

Friday morning came and we all went to school. When we walked into the office, the secretary smiled at us and mom and dad had to sign their names on a clipboard with our school colors and get a fancy red apple sticker to wear. The principal greeted us and showed us to his office. I couldn't believe it, there was my teacher sitting in his office, too, by the round table. I said, "I like Triple T the best." Dad said, "Hush Little Bit." My teacher giggled and whispered that she does, too.

My teacher started talking about how kind, respectful, and caring I am in class and with my friends. She said she was super proud of me for passing my math facts so quickly, but then she stopped smiling and started looking really sad. She told them she thought I might have a reading problem. And if they agreed I would need to take some test with some other folks to see if this was true.

"Noooooooooo, I can't do that. Remember you have to help me with reading tests?" I looked at mom and dad and couldn't believe what I was hearing it sounded like everyone was yelling really loud, "Yesssssssssssssss!" What? What are you thinking? I read slow and leave letters out. I must have looked really scared because mom reached for my hand under the table and just held it.

Another week went by and this tall cowboy type of guy came into the room and in a deep train voice called my name. The teacher gave me a smile and a nod as if to say, "It's okay, go ahead." As we left the classroom, he put his cowboy hat back on and said, "Let's go to the library and play a few games." I really liked how his cowboy boots clicked on the hallway floor. I told him I liked the band on his hat. He said it was from a real rattlesnake. *Yikes*!

I tried not to laugh out loud when he spoke but his voice just sounded like a train. He was really nice and never said hurry up. In no time we were walking back to my classroom and he told me I worked really hard, I had done good job!

The week before Christmas break my teacher gave me another letter to take home to my parents. Once again, she said, "It's a nice note, don't worry." When mom and dad opened it, they quickly read over it and said it was another meeting, but I didn't need to go.

On the day of the meeting, I saw the tall train-sounding cowboy standing by the office. I wondered if he was waiting for mom and dad, but I had to go to class and couldn't ask him. At the meeting, he told mom and dad I had a reading disability and they had a plan to help me learn how to read better. When the teacher came back into the classroom, she called me up to my desk and said the meeting went really well and they had all agreed to try something new. She reassured me it would be awesome, but mom and dad would tell me all about it when I got home from school. And if I had any questions to be sure and ask her in the morning.

When mom and dad picked me up from school, they were giggling because they had a surprise for me. Tonight, they said, "We are having dessert first. We are going to Pie Haven. "PIE HAVEN!", I screamed. Pie Haven is my favorite of favorite places. They have cinnamon ice cream that goes on top of apple pie which is my second favorite pie! "I love you guys! Yippee!"

When we sat down to eat dad said, "Little Bit", we are going to tell you about the meeting we had at your school today."

"So," mom started, "the tall cowboy man told us you are very smart and did great, but then he said you have a reading disability and there is another reading teacher at your school who wants to help you learn how to read and spell better."

Mom took a napkin and wrote the letter P I E and she asked what does that spell, I told her pie. "Yes, that's right, but if we move these letters around it can make another word, I E P." I had no clue what that word was. Mom said, "Just say the letters." So, I did.

"It says I E P"

"Right," she said. "Let me explain. I is for individual-that's you. E is for education—this is why you go to school,—to learn. And P is for plan. It's like a blueprint on how the teachers are going to help you. Remember when you were trying to put the birdhouse together but couldn't until you looked at the blueprint? Well, IEP is very similar, it is a guide, too. The new reading teacher would like for you to join her reading group right after Christmas break. What do you think?"

What do I think? I thought where have these people been all of my life! I started jumping up and down in my seat. Then I got really scared! Mom and dad said my new reading teacher is best friends with my teacher. They both love reading and teaching children how to read. I whispered, "I will try."

World Map

USA Map

Well, Christmas break came and went and I was a little nervous about going back to school to have a new reading teacher. But mom and dad gave me a poster with a world map with a saying from Dr. Seuss, that read, "The more that you read, the more things you will know, the more that you learn, the more places you'll go."[1] I liked that poster because I had circled several places on the map I would like to go. So, off to sleep I went the night before my first day back to school after Christmas break.

I went to my classroom just like always. We always did math first, then reading, so, when it came to reading time my teacher called my name and asked me to come up to her desk with my favorite pencil. My favorite pencil was the yellow one with the United States Map wrapped around it. She said, "It's time for you to go to your new reading class and it is right next door." I asked her if she would walk with me and she did. I wasn't scared, I just wasn't sure which next door she was talking about. When we got to the door, I stopped her and said, "I can do this, I'm brave!" And I really thought, *I just want to read and write better, so how bad can this be*? On the outside of the door was a huge red, white, and black poster that said, "YOU CAN and YOU WILL! So, for five seconds I thought, *I can read and write and I will learn how to read and write better. No more being scared, I got this…let's do it* and I walked in with a gigantic smile.

Her room was amazing. She had taken yellow pool noodles and made them like yellow #2 pencils and had them hung all over the room with little posters hanging from the middle of the pencil that started with, "The point is…" "You can do this, you're a rock star" or, "Don't wish for it Work for it." And my favorite was, "Use your eraser it belongs with the pencil." I really like her. She likes to smile and uses silly voices to get us to try something new. I think her favorite shirt is the one with the letters L-O-V-E in a square, colored just like her door poster. When we have free time, she tells us funny stories especially ones about softball. I told her my mom used to play softball, but she's too old to play now.

Now when it is reading time, I gather my materials and head next door, I just can't wait to see what we will be doing next. This teacher's reading time is just like my first reading class. Instead of the Daily Five we have 3C time which is a three-center rotation…independent time, computer time, and one-on-one time (that's my favorite). During independent time we can listen to a story on an iPod, draw pictures about the story, write a different ending for the story or we can use letter stamps and practice spelling our spelling words. But on Friday's it's "Fun Friday" and we can use shaving cream to spell our spelling words when we practice taking our spelling test. Spelling tests are on Monday's, she says it gives us more practice time at home. Woo-hoo! At computer time we can choose to sit at a desk computer or have the iPad at our desk. I can finally play some of the games I saw my friends play in my first reading class. Really, all three centers are my favorite, and time goes by so fast. One time my reading teacher told us we were going to have a play. The play was about being a secret agent and we were the agents who actually went around the school doing random acts of kindness but never got caught. The funniest time was when we got stuck by the big dumpster waiting for the custodian to go back into his office. That was so close. I never knew reading and real adventures could be so much fun together!

By spring break, I had read all of the orange and pink books. I could answer almost all of the questions and my spelling was really improving. I really like my new reading teacher; she doesn't use red when she grades our papers. She uses all the other colors.

And by the end of the year, I wrote my very first story about Narwhals and Secret Agents. This year was as sweet as apple PIE.

Endnotes

[1] *I Can Read with My Eyes Shut*, by Dr. Seuss, Harper Collins, October 12, 1978.

About the Author

Peggy Howard, a retired public-school elementary special education teacher, has shared many tearful reading lessons as well as celebrated those "I got it!" moments. She received her Bachelor's Degree from Eastern Illinois University (with a dual major in general and special education) and a Master's Degree from Olivet Nazarene University. She and her husband love to ride bikes and play with their five grandchildren. She lives in O'Fallon, Illinois.

CPSIA information can be obtained
at www.ICGtesting.com
Printed in the USA
BVHW020243091221
623422BV00019BB/1153